DOPIN' DAN
IN WORLD WAR 3
©1981 BY TED RICHARDS

THIS APOCALYPTIC TALE OF ARMAGEDDON BEGAN THE DAY PVT. D. DAN WAS ASSIGNED SPECIAL DUTY AS A TANK RADIO OPERATER FOR THE ANNUAL N.A.T.O DEFENSE MANEUVERS ON THE EAST/WEST GERMAN BORDER....
(WHEW) ONLY ONE MORE WEEK OF "OPERATION CHICKEN" THEN IT'S FRANKFURT HERE I COME!!!
HUH?
KNOW YOUR ENEMY
THE SOVIET SOLDIER TRAINS 60 HOURS PER WEEK IN FULL UNIFORM.
HE FIRES 3 TYPES OF WEAPONS AND CAN DO THREE JOBS.
HE IS NOT ALLOWED TO SURRENDER AND IF CAPTURED WILL VOLUNTEER NO INFORMATION.
HE CAN LIVE ON POTATO GRUEL FOR ONE MONTH.
HE CAN MANUALLY OPERATE ALL OF HIS EQUIPMENT IF REQUIRED.
YEOW! HOW COME WE'RE MESSIN' WITH THESE GUYS!
SEVERAL DAYS LATER, THE ANNUAL CONFRONTATION BEGINS. BUT THIS TIME THE "N.A.T.O. COMMANDERS" HAVE DEVISED OPERATION CHICKEN TO SCARE THE FORMIDABLE "WARSAW PACT" FORCES...

THE WARSAW TANKS HURL THEMSELVES AT THE THIN NATO LINE — BUT WAIT! THE NATO TANKS HURL THEMSELVES AT THE WARSAW TANKS. THE TENSION IS UNBEARABLE! NO ONE CAN TAKE-IT ANY LONGER — —THEY'RE HITTING THEIR FAILSAFE BUTTONS!
BUT UH OH! DOPIN' DAN'S EARPHONES ARE PLUGGED INTO HIS TAPEDECK!
A LONE TANK PLUNGES ACROSS THE FRONTIER!
SEX AND DRUGS AND ROCK'N' ROLL
HELL WITH IT! ATTACK! ATTACK! IT'S OUR ONLY CHANCE!
NO! NO! WAIT 'TIL THEY FIRE!
CRAZY AMERICANS!
NAIL 'EM!
SMASH THEM! SMASH ZEE KAPITALIST SWINE!!
NO! NO! IT IS A TRICK!
SEX AND DRUGS AND ROCK'N' ROLL — THE FORCES THAT DRIVE PVT. DAN'S TANK DEEPER AND DEEPER INTO ENEMY TERRITORY!

VOOSH
VOOSH
FWAP
FWAP
CRONK
GRAK
A SANDBLAST MISSLE DESTROYED TH' TURBINE ENGINE IN OUR MILLION DOLLAR CHRYSLER TANK!
AFFIRMATIVE— THE COMPUTER SAYS WE HAVE TO FILL OUT RA 711-TANK SALVAGE FORM!
FIRST, WE HAD BETTER MOVE TO A SECURE AREA!
YEAH— BEFORE WE START WORLD WAR III!
OH NO! TOO LATE!

SGT. TURDY! ARE WE AT WAR? IS THIS FOR REAL?
RIGHT-ON MEATHEAD! IT'S THE SUPER BOWL!
C'MON! WE'RE GONNA KICK SOME RUSSIAN BUTTS!
HERE! YOU NEED TO LOAD UP WITH SOME MAIN COMBAT GEAR- LASER GUIDED SKIN BURNER- PSYCHO MIND PROJECTOR- TANK SMELTER -SATELLITE-LAUNCHER...
PUNCH OUT THOSE GUNSHIPS ON YOUR COMPUTER FIRE CONTROL-
I'LL KNOCK OUT THAT SQUADRON OF TANKS.
C'MON IVAN! SHOW ME WHAT YOU GOT!

THE BATTLE EXPLODES INTO A FULL SCALE WAR AS BOTH SIDES UNLEASH THIRTY YEARS WORTH OF BOMBS BULLETS, TANKS, FIGHTERS, AND ALIENATED YOUTH!
PVT. D. DAN, PROUD FIGHTING MEMBER OF THE 82ND AIRBORNE DIVISION, TAKES TEN!
C'MON! NUKE ME! HAHAHA NUKE ME!
I THINK I GOT A BAD CASE OF BATTLE FATIGUE..
A LULL SETTLES OVER THE BATTLE FIELD — TIME TO REST AND RE-ARM...
HEY! MY TAPEDECK STILL WORKS!! ...LET'S SEE- HMM... "GROUND ZERO"... "THE BASH"....
?
I THINK I'LL WRITE A LETTER TO MY MOM...
GIVE ME TAPEDECK.
?

UH... SURE. HERE. TAKE TH' TAPEDECK —GOOD TAPES TOO!
UH, UM, I GOT A PAIR OF LEVIS JEANS IN MY SURVIVAL PARK— —LET ME GO—AND THEY'RE YOURS!
UH... O.K. I TAKE LEVIS YOU GO!
HERE. YOU TAKE SOME VODKA — GET PLENTY DRUNK— EVERYBODY DEAD OUTSIDE!
REALLY? NO KIDDING?
—HEY LOOK. WE MIGHT AS WELL JUST HANG OUT AND PARTY 'TIL WE DIE OR FIND SOMEONE...
HA HA HA HA SURE! WE FIND SOME CHICKS— BOOGEY—BOOGEY! HA HA HA HA!
HERE! I SHOW YOU HOW WE DRINK VODKA IN RUSSIA!
GLUG
GLUG
—WANNA SEE HOW WE GET LOADED?!
HOW DO YOU LIKE THAT AMERICAN CIGARETTE?
DA! LOOK! IT MAKE MY HEAD FEEL FUNNY LIKE AMERICAN MICKEY MOUSE!
HAHA HAHA

HEY! YOU'RE ALL RIGHT! HOW COME WE'RE FIGHTING EACH OTHER??
I TELL YOU WHY!
YOU 'PIG' AMERICANS TAKE EVERYTHING IN THE WORLD! OIL! COFFEE! SLAVES! THEN YOU HAVE BIG COCAINE PARTY WHILE EVERYBODY STARVE!
AH, YOU GUYS JUST WANT THE SAME THING — YOU'RE NO BETTER! SLAVE LABOR CAMPS! SECRET POLICE! NO FREEDOM. NO ROCK'N'ROLL. NO SEX! NO LEVIS JEANS!
?
DA! WHAT WE FIGHTING FOR!...
RIGHT! HERE-HAVE ANOTHER AMERICAN CIGARETTE...
-AND LET'S WHIP THIS WORLD WAR 3
(HA! IS THIS TH' BEST THEY CAN DO?)
C'MON! KNOCK IT OFF! TH' PARTY'S OVER!
SGT. TURDY?
SGT. MEATKOV!
WHIP IT
WHIP IT
GET IT STRAIGHT
WHIP IT INTO SHAPE
WHIP IT

WHAT HAPPENED? - IS THE WORLD WIPED OUT! DID ANYBODY WIN THE WAR?
AH, IT ENDED UP A TIE —WE ONLY BLEW AWAY HALF THE EARTH BEFORE THEY CUT A DEAL...
—WE CARVED UP TH' PIE THEN AGREED WE COULD POUND OUT ALL WE WANT FROM OUR OWN SHARES AS LONG AS WE SPLIT THE LOOT WITH FREE TRADE "AGREEMENTS"—HA!
?
BUT ALL OUR VOLUNTEERS WERE KILLED, SO, UNTIL THE DRAFT TAKES EFFECT—
—YOU'RE GOING TO EL SALVADOR, THEN MEXICO!
DA! AND YOU GO TO AFGHANISTAN, THEN IRAN!!
MEANWHILE ON THE HOME FRONT, THE DRAFT SQUADS HIT THE LOCAL HOT SPOTS...
THE BOMB SHELTER
ALL RIGHT! LISTEN UP! EVERYONE IN CAMOUFLAGE CLOTHING—MOVE TO THE RIGHT...
C'MON, "SANDINISTA", YOU CAN TRADE YOUR GUITAR IN FOR A GUN!
WELL, AT LEAST WE WON'T HAVE TO PRETEND NOW...
THE END

TODAY'S ARMY WITH DOPIN' DAN
(IN) "SICK CALL"
BY TED RICHARDS
©1979 BY TED RICHARDS
PVT. DOPIN' DAN?
SICK CALL: 0800–1100 HRS FILLOUT FORM FBS1821061-213 SIT — WAIT
RIGHT HERE...
X-RO
HI, PVT. DAN, I'M DR. KLUTZ — HOW DO YOU FEEL.... ANY "PROBLEMS" YOU WANT TO TALK ABOUT?
NO WAY, DOC — I'M JUST PLAIN SICK. MUSCLES ACHE, FEEL HOT 'N' FEVERISH, MY CHEST HURTS...
HMMM, WELL, YOU DO EXHIBIT FLU-LIKE SYMPTOMS - HMM I HEAR SOME LOWER CHEST CONGESTION..
UH, I'LL BE RIGHT BACK, O.K.?
OH-KAY-Y.. HMM.. ... LOWER CONGESTION.. .. LOWER CONGESTION... .. PULMONARY... HMM WHAT DOES PULMONARY DEGENEROSIS MEAN? HMM... HMMM...
FLIP FLIP FLIP
UH, EXCUSE ME COL. CHAINSAW — I HAVE A PATIENT WHO NEEDS A PULMONARY DEGENEROSIS TEST... WHAT DOES THAT MEAN - AND HOW DO I DO-IT?..
AHH - DON'T BOTHER - JUST DO A MENINGITIS TEST — THAT'S ALL WE'RE WORRIED ABOUT..

NOW THIS IS JUST A LITTLE SPINAL TAP..
WHOOPS! I FORGOT TO SCREW THE NEEDLE IN- I-I'LL BE RIGHT BACK—O.K.?
CRACK
O.K., READY- AGH! NYAH! (WHEW) IT REALLY IS STUCK! WE'LL HAVE TO OPERATE!
THERE! FROM NOW ON, Lt. KLUTZ, PUT THE NEEDLE BETWEEN THE SPINAL DISCS—NOT IN THEM!
YES, B-B-B-BUT WE MADE A MISTAKE, SIR...
-THIS PERSON ISN'T PVT. DOPIN' DAN!
WHAT! THEN WHERE IS PVT. DAN?!!
PVT. DAN?- HE'S RIGHT HERE! WE JUST PREFORMED AN APPENDECTOMY ON HIM.....
HE'S DOIN' QUITE WELL...
TWO DAYS LATER-
I HEARD YOU RECOVERED FROM YOUR OPERATION IN A SINGLE DAY! GOOD SOLDIER! THAT'S A RECORD!
YEAH... BUT I STILL GOT TH' FLU!

TODAY'S ARMY WITH DOPIN' DAN
©1979 BY TED RICHARDS
NOW YOU LOOK LIKE REAL SOLDIERS WITH YOUR NEW HAIRCUTS!
HERE'S YOUR THREE-DAY PASSES..
WHO ELSE LOOKS LIKE THIS, EXCEPT G.I.'S?
LOOK LIKE A SOLDIER
SOME DEAL— NEW G.I. STYLE HAIRCUTS FOR THREE DAY PASSES.
YEAH—ALL TH' DECENT WOMEN WILL STILL KNOW WE'RE G.I.'S!
YEAH—SCREW-IT! WE'RE G.I.'S—RIGHT?! SO WHY TRY TO HIDE-IT!? LET'S GO DOWNTOWN AND BE G.I.'S—REAL G.I.'S!!!
RIGHT—ON! WHAT DO WE GOT TO LOSE?!
SO A FEW HOURS LATER
PIZZA
RECORDS · BOOKS · PIPES ·
HOUSE OF ZONK
HA HA HA LOOK AT ALL TH' G.I.'S!
HEY! IT'S NO USE SUCKERS! TH' WHOLE TOWN KNOWS YOU'RE IN TH' ARMY!
HEY-THIS JOINT LOOKS INTERESTIN'...
THE DAMAGE CLUB

??
THIS WHOLE PLACE AIN'T GOIN' NO WHERE: I'M BORED AND CRAZY DON'T MESS WIT' ME:
THIS PO-GO DANCIN' IS NOTHIN' FOR A PARATROOPER!
YOU LOOK JUST LIKE REAL GI'S! I LOVE IT!!
YEAH, IT'S A NEAT IMAGE..
YEAH, WE WORK AT IT...
NEXT DAY, THE WORD IS OUT!
YOUR "LOOK LIKE A SOLDIER" CAMPAIGN IS A TOTAL SUCCESS, SGT. TURDY....
UH, YES SIR, BUT SOMETHIN' SCREWY IS GOIN' ON, AND I CAN'T QUITE PUT MY FINGER ON IT...

TODAY'S ARMY
©1980 BY TED RICHARDS
GENERAL WHEELCHAIR! WE'RE ON A RED ALERT! REPORT TO THE WAR ROOM, SIR!
HUH! WELL I'LL BE ☆@#%!!
THIS BETTER BE KOSHER BECAUSE I WAS SHOOTING ONE HELL OF A @☆# GAME!!
PUT YOUR UNIFORM ON, SIR...
WHAT'S GOING ON? ANOTHER HOSTAGE RESCUE I DON'T KNOW ABOUT?
NO. THE RUSSIANS HAVE LAUNCHED A PRE-EMPTIVE NUCLEAR STRIKE!
OFF ON
WAR ROOM
WHAT! WELL BY GOD LET'S BLOW THEM AWAY-Y!
THAT'S AN ORDER...
THE D.W.I.M.W.I.T.* COMPUTER INDICATES LOSSES OF 10 AND 17 POINTS ON THE EAST COAST TOTAL SCORE IS: U.S.S.R. - 157 U.S.A. - 108
BY GOD, WE'RE LOSING! LAUNCH WARHEADS ON THEIR GERM WARFARE CENTER AND K.G.B. BUNKER!
* DEFENSIVE WARTIME IMMEDIATE WORLWIDE TARGET SYSTEM.

WE SCORED 86 POINTS ON RESERVE LAUNCH. D.W.I.M.W.I.T. SHOWS THE SOVIETS SCORED 40 POINTS WITH DIRECT HITS ON BEVERLY HILLS AND EXXON OIL!
☆@#!*!! THAT'S 197 TO 194!!! WE'RE STILL LOSING BY THREE!!
DOOT DIT
DAAZT
DOOT DOOT
DIT DIT DAT
WE'LL CONTAMINATE THEIR WATER SUPPLY, PLUS ERADICATE POLAND, IRAN AND VIET-NAM HA HA HA — AND ALL THEIR CHILD CARE CENTERS! HA HA HA HA
D.W.I.M.W.I.T. INDICATES RETALIATION ON ALL SHOPPING MALLS AND RECREATION VEHICLES
DOW DAZ DIZ
DOP DOP DOP
BIP BIP BIP
BIB BIB DAAZ
D.W.I.M.W.I.T. PROJECTS A SCORE OF 76 POINTS U.S.A. — 70 POINTS U.S.S.R.
THAT'S IT! WAHOOOOO WE WIN! WE WIN! WE WIN!!!
GENERAL WHEELCHAIR! THIS WAR WAS A COMPUTER MALFUNCTION! WE WERE OPERATING ON A SIMULATED PROGRAM. — NOTHING HAPPENED!
NOTHING?
ABORT
WHO CARES! WE WON DIDN'T WE??!!
GET ME MY GOLF CLUBS!

TODAY'S ARMY WITH DOPIN' DAN
" A SOLDIERS' CHRISTMAS "
BY TED RICHARDS
©1979 BY TED RICHARDS
TH' LOWEST! GUARD DUTY ON CHRISTMAS EVE---
" PEACE ON EARTH, GOODWILL TO ALL MEN " — WHAT A JOKE!
YEAH, I KNOW WHAT YOU MEAN- CHRISTMAS IS A BITCH FOR A SOLDIER...
I'LL SAY! NO HOME, NO FAMILY, NO GIRLFRIEND, NO PRESENTS..
HEY, WAIT A MINUTE — WHO ARE YOU - SOME KIND OF WEIRD CHRISTMAS SPIRIT?
HAHA - NO, I'M JUST THE OL' UNIVERSAL SOLDIER PULLIN' SOME "COSMIC C.Q."*
* CHARGE OF QUARTERS
CHRISTMAS SPIRIT ONLY VISITS BANKERS AND CORPORATE EXECUTIVES- MY JOB IS TO CHEER UP YOU GRUNTS ON CHRISTMAS EVE...
WELL, YOU GOT YOUR WORK CUT OUT- I'VE GOT ORDERS "TO SHOOT TO KILL" ON CHRISTMAS EVE- BAD NEWS, HUH?
THAT'S NOTHIN'- YOU SHOULD'VE BEEN THERE WHEN WE CRUCIFIED CHRIST....
YEAH, WELL, WE DID TH' MAI LAI MASSACRE IN VIET NAM..

AH, SHAKE-IT OFF— SOME HOSTILE ALIENS COULD LAND TOMORROW AND IF YOU WHIP'EM GOOD, YOU'LL ALL BE HEROS AGAIN!
YEAGH
-LOOK AT IT THIS WAY: YOU WIN SOME, YOU LOSE SOME— ALL YOU CAN DO IS FIGHT AND HOPE FOR TH' BEST...
HUH...
WHICH REMINDS ME — I GOTTA GO BASH SOME HEADS AT AN ANTI-NUCLEAR POWER PLANT DEMONSTRATION...
-THEN AFTER THAT, GO CONQUER TH' MEXICAN OIL FIELDS — THEN GUARD A CONCENTRATION CAMP IN SIBERIA— THEN BLOW UP A BUS OF CIVILIANS - BOMB A REFUGEE CAMP...
WHICH REMINDS ME — I GOTTA MAKE UP A SHORT-TIMERS CALENDER...

TODAY'S ARMY WITH DOPIN' DAN
BY TED RICHARDS
(WHEW) THIS ENERGY CRISIS IS FREAKIN' ME OUT! I HAVEN'T BEEN OFF FT. FRAGG FOR 3 WEEKS!
YEAH, AND THE PLACE STINKS OF G.I.'S SINCE THEY CUT OFF TH' AIR CONDITIONING!
©1979 BY TED RICHARDS
YOU CAN'T EVEN GET ON THE BUS TO FATALBURG...
FATALBURG
I GOT-IT! LET'S GO A.W.O.L.!
O.K., I'M GAME — LET'S FLY OUTTA HERE!
I'M SORRY, BUT ALL OUR FLIGHTS ARE BOOKED, HOWEVER, WE DO HAVE WIDE-BODY DC-10 SERVICE AVAILABLE.....
UH, NO THANKS..
TRY TH' AMTRACK TRAIN!
I'M SORRY, BUT ALL AMTRACK SERVICE IS BOOKED THREE MONTHS IN ADVANCE. THIS IS A RECORDING..
W-WE CAN'T EVEN GO AWOL...
YAAHGH BLIBBLE BLIBBLE BLIBBLE

KRUGA KRUGA KRUGA
ALERT! ALERT! WE'RE JUMPING OFF INTO IRAN AT 0200 HRS.!
OH NO! IRAN?! WE'RE GONNA DIE!
HEY! IT'S O.K.! AT LEAST WE'LL GET OUTTA HERE!!
-AT 1740 HRS WE LINK UP WITH THE 502ND AND 118TH BRIGADE..
-THE SHAH WILL TURN TH' OIL BACK ON AT 1830 HRS. WE HOLD OUR POSITIONS 'TIL 2140 HRS...
1 SHAH RETURNS TO POWER
2 AYATOLLAH RETURNED TO PARIS
3 FRANCE GIVEN FREE OIL
82ND ABN DISTRIBUTES BATHING SUITS
WONKA WONKA WONKA
WHUP! TH'ALERT'S BEEN CALLED OFF! STRIP DOWN—AS YOU WERE—STANDBY FOR 24 HOURS!
5 101ST ABN DISTRIBUTES ROCK 'N' ROLL TAPES
7 82ND ABN PULLS OUT WHEN OIL DROPS TO $10.00 PER BARREL
11 PRESIDENT HOLDS PRESS CONFERENCE IN SMALLBURG, OHIO
I BET THEY DIDN'T HAVE TH' FUEL TO FLY US OVER THERE...
I'M GONNA FLIP...
I-I CAN'T TAKE-IT!
DON'T LOOSE YOUR COOL—THIS WHOLE SCENE GAVE ME AN IDEA!
LATER
HEY, THAT'S SOME CAR Y'GOT THERE—HOW'S IT RUN?
IT RUNS ON U.S.B.S.—THERE'LL NEVER BE A SHORTAGE OF THAT STUFF!

TODAY'S ARMY
BY TED RICHARDS
A'RIGHT! SHAPE UP! GENERAL WHEELCHAIR'S HERE TO TAKE COMMAND OF PROJECT PSYCHO!
HA! THE NEW CODE WORD FOR THE ARMY!
COPYRIGHT © 1979 BY TED RICHARDS
GENTLEMEN, YOU ARE LOOKING AT A PSYCHO-WHAMMER, THE MOST SOPHISTICATED WEAPON EVER TO BE TESTED BY THE UNITED STATES ARMY...
THE PSYCHO WHAMMER IS CAPABLE OF EMMITING POWERFUL MENTO-WAVES THAT CAUSE NAUSEA AND DEPRESSION IN THE ENEMY...
THE WEAPON HAS BEEN AIMED AT A HIDDEN CONTROL GROUP OF TYPICAL OFFICERS AND ENLISTED MEN...
GENTLEMEN, BEGIN PROJECT PSYCHO!
DWOOO

GEE BEE WEE WEE WEE WEE
WAIT! WE'VE GOT FEEDBACK! (GAPH) STOP! THAT'S AN ORDER! STOP!
GLORP
BLURP
SGT. TURDY!? WHY AREN'T YOU ILL?
ER, UH, ACCORDING TO FIELD CONTROL, THE PSYCHO-WHAMMER ONLY AFFECTED TH' OFFICERS, SIR...
- THEN THE PSYCHO-WHAMMER IS INOPERABLE - RIGHT, GENTLEMEN?!
RIGHT, SIR!!
?
UH, I BEG TH' GENERAL'S PARDON, BUT TH' PSYCHO-WHAMMER DESTROYED TH' ENEMY OFFICERS... AND WELL, IT DID TH' JOB! - IT'S A FANTASTIC WEAPON!!!
THAT'S ENOUGH SGT. TURDY - REPORT TO ME IN TEN MINUTES!!
LATER
SGT. TURDY... WE JUST WANT TO LET YOU KNOW WE AGREED WITH YOUR EVALUATION OF THE PSYCHO-WHAMMER...
YEAH, EXCEPT WE'D REDESIGN IT SO I'D MAKE TH' OFFICERS FLIP OUT! AND SHOOT EACH OTHER!
SHHH! KNOCK IT OFF! NOTHING HAPPENED TODAY! NOTHING! THAT'S AN ORDER!!
HQ
HQ 52 G-2

TODAY'S ARMY
WITH DOPIN' DAN
©1980 BY TED RICHARDS
THE "MOONLITE BRIGADE"
HEY, GUNNER - HOW ABOUT LENDIN' ME TWENTY BUCKS -TIL PAYDAY...
UH-SURE!
HA - TWENTY BUCKS IS NOTHIN' THESE DAYS - HOW'D YOU LIKE TO EARN SOME BIG MONEY FOR A CHANGE?
A'RIGHT, HERE'S TH' GIG - YOU CAN JOIN OUR TROOP OF "PART-TIME" SOLDIERS OF FORTUNE CALLED TH' MOONLITE BRIGADE...
FAR-OUT, I'LL TRY ANYTHING ONCE---
THAT NIGHT.
THERE'S OUR XC-200 P.D.Q.* TRANSPORT. WE GOTTA CONTRACT IN BOOMBAWWE, AFRICA, TONIGHT..
Y'GOT TO BE PUTTIN' ME ON...
C'MON YOU'LL SEE...
* PRETTY DAMN QUICK
1
THIS XC-200 P.D.Q IS A NEW TOP SECRET S.T.O.L., SUPERSONIC, MACH 5, MAIN BATTLE SUPPORT AIRCRAFT THAT'S MADE IN FRANCE...
2
HANG ON - WE'RE BOOSTING UP TO MACH 5 - WE'LL HIT BOOMBAWWE IN ABOUT FORTY MINUTES!
SWIP
YEP... THIS IS TH' ONLY JOB TH' ARMY REALLY TRAINS YOU FOR....
RIGHT, THEN THEY GIVE ALL TH' MONEY TO THE GUYS WHO MAKE TH' GUNS!
I'LL DRINK TO THAT...
ZZZ
SGT. TURDY ???!!
HEY-YOU THINK YOU'RE SHORT OF CASH-TRY FEEDIN' FIVE KIDS ON ARMY PAY!!
(URP!) WE'VE HIT TH' DROP POINT!
FOP

C'MON - WE'RE FIGHTIN' FOR TH' POPULAR TRIBAL FRONT T'NIGHT.
ARE THEY TH' GOOD GUYS OR BAD GUYS?
WHO GIVES A @*#*!!! JUST SHOOT T'KILL AND YOU'LL BE A'RIGHT!
HERE - IF YOU'RE CAPTURED, TAKE THIS SUICIDE CAPSULE - IT'LL CHEAT 'EM OUT OF THEIR KICKS WHEN THEY GET A HOLD OF MERCENARY PRISONERS....
WHUPS! TIME TO EARN OUR WAGES!
BUDDA BUDDA BOOT
AND ON AND ON THROUGH THE NIGHT.
C'MON - WE GOTTA SCRAMBLE, OR WE'LL NEVER MAKE IT BACK IN TIME FOR REVEILLE*!
* THE BUGLE CALL THAT BEGINS EACH MILITARY DAY
LATER THE NEXT DAY BACK AT FT. FRAGG...
WANNA MAKE ANOTHER GO OF IT TONIGHT?
UH.. NAW. I GOT ENOUGH TO LAST ME 'TIL PAYDAY
ZZZ

TODAY'S ARMY
BY TED RICHARDS
LISTEN UP BUCK- GEN. WHEELCHAIR'S INSPECTIN' TH' HOUSING AREA TODAY, SO I WANT THAT LAWN MOWED, RAKED AND TRIMMED BY 1100 HRS SHARP! YOU HEAR ME?
AH-DON'T SWEAT-IT DAD- I'LL DO-IT...
TURDY
A'RIGHT- HERE'S FIVE DOLLARS IN CASE YOU NEED GAS AND YOU CAN KEEP TH' CHANGE IF YOU DO A GOOD JOB.
HEY, THANKS DAD!
HMM... THERE MIGHT NOT BE ENOUGH GAS - I'LL GO GET SOME MORE - AND SEE IF I CAN CON SOMEONE AT TH' P.X. INTO SELLING ME SOME BEER...
©1980 BY TED RICHARDS
HEY BUCK-WANNA GO SEE IF WE CAN CRASH TH' OFFICER'S POOL? JANIE WHEELCHAIR'S* HAVIN' AN ALL DAY POOL PARTY!
AW NAW- I GOTTA CUT TH' LAWN BEFORE 11 O'CLOCK OR MY OL' MAN'S GONNA KILL ME....
* GENERAL WHEELCHAIR'S DAUGHTER
HEY C'MON — I HEARD THEY AIN'T INSPECTIN' BASTOGNE GABLES* 'TIL 2 P.M.! WE GOT PLENTY OF TIME!!
UH, A'RIGHT, BUT I'LL HAVE TO SPLIT EARLY.
* THE NAME OF BUCK TURDY'S HOUSING AREA
ONE HOUR LATER—
YOU BOYS KNOW ENLISTED DEPENDENTS ARE NOT ALLOWED IN THE OFFICER'S POOL- NOW BEAT-IT!
C'MON- I KNOW A G.I. WHO'LL BUY US SOME BEER AT TH' SNACK BAR!
GIGGLE
HA HA HA
SPLASH
OFFICER'S POOL
MEANWHILE
I SHOULD'VE NEVER GIVEN BUCK THAT FIVE DOLLARS. I'D BETTER CHECK-UP ON HIM....

HUH! I KNEW IT! HE HASN'T TOUCHED ONE ✩◎# BLADE OF GRASS!!
THIS IS TH' LAST ◎✩# STRAW! I'M SHIPPIN' THAT #✩◎ PUNK OFF TO A MILITARY ACADEMY!
BRRAA
WHACK HACK CHOP
BROOOM
WHAT TH'- STOP! STOP THIS VEHICLE!!
SGT. TURDY, I'M ANXIOUS TO HEAR AN EXPLA----
OH NO! THAT'S TH' GENERAL'S JEEP!!!
BRRR
CONFOUND IT! I NEVER THOUGHT I'D EARN MY PURPLE HEART INSPECTING LAWNS!!
I'VE GOT A DEPENDENT ON TH' LINE WHO CLAIMS HIS "OLD MAN" IS ON THE FRONT STEPS WITH A MACHETTE!
SOUNDS LIKE ANOTHER "LAWN INSPECTION CRISIS"...
CRISIS SEC
FAMILY SERVICES

TODAY'S ARMY WITH DOPIN' DAN
HOW COME YOU'RE PICKING UP CIGARETTE BUTTS - YOU'RE A RADIO OPERATOR — YOU'RE SUPPOSED TO BE PICKING UP BEER CANS.
THEY GOT MY M.O.S.* ALL FOULED UP - PERSONNEL LOST MY RECORDS AND THEY CAN'T DO ANYTHING UNTIL THEY FIND THEM....
©1979 BY TED RICHARDS
*MILITARY OCCUPATION SPECIALTY
AH, THAT'S A BUNCH OF BULL - C'MON, LET'S GO OVER TO PERSONNEL AND SHOW 'EM WHO'S RUNNIN' THIS ARMY...
WELL, GOOD LUCK... THAT PLACE IS REALLY OUT OF IT...
SGT. BOILER, WE GOT A LITTLE "PROBLEM" WITH PVT. DOPIN' DAN - HIS M.O.S. IS FOULED UP AND I WANT IT STRAIGHTEND OUT, A.S.A.P. - WHICH MEANS RIGHT NOW...
YES, SGT. TURDY... I'M FAMILIAR WITH THE "PROBLEM"! HIS RECORDS ARE MISSING AND NOTHING CAN BE DONE AT THIS TIME...
ALL THE PROPER FORMS AND PROCEDURES HAVE BEEN INITIATED - DD FORM 2101, "LOCATER REQUEST" HAS BEEN COMPLETED, RA FORM 99, "FILE 13" HAS BEEN DATED. SEE. EVERYTHING'S IN ORDER. NOTHING CAN BE DONE UNTIL WE LOCATE HIS RECORDS...
LOOK, SGT. BOILER - YOU FIND THEM ☆@*!!:!☆☆ RECORDS, OR I'M GONNA SHOW YOU WHO'S RUNNING THIS ☆@* ARMY!!!
WHAM

DON'T YOU THREATEN ME! SGT. TURDY... I RUN THIS ☆@&#!* ARMY — AND DON'T YOU FORGET IT — OR, I'LL SEND YOU AND YOUR RECORDS TO ANTARTICA!
GROWL!
A'RIGHT- PLAY IT YOUR WAY, SGT. BOILER — I'LL BE BACK!
C'MON — WE GOTTA LINE UP SOME FIREPOWER! (MUMBLE, CURSE) WHEN I GET THROUGH WITH HER, SHE'LL BE SAYIN', "HOW MUCH, WHAT KIND, AND WHAT COLOR"?!?!
—AND SHE JUST BLATANTLY REFUSED TO RECTIFY THE "PROBLEM"?
'AT'S RIGHT, GEN. WHEELCHAIR — HIS RECORDS HAVE BEEN LOST FOR OVER SIX MONTHS - WE CAN'T EVEN GIVE HIM CAREER COUNSELING!
WELL, WHO DO YOU THINK RUNS THIS ☆@&#! ARMY? ME OR YOU? NOW GET OUT OF HERE BEFORE I SHIP YOUR RECORDS STRAIGHT TO TH' NORTH POLE!
— MAYBE SANTA CLAUS WILL BRING YOU YOUR NEXT STAR!
WE GOT BETTER THINGS TO DO - HOW'S THE IRANIAN STRIKE PLAN? WE GOTTA SHOW 'EM WHO'S BOSS....
RIGHT..
LOOK- FORGET ABOUT THE RECORDS. AT LEAST WE'RE GETTING PAID ON TIME — RIGHT?..
RIGHT...
WHATEVER HAPPENED TO DOPIN' DAN'S RECORDS???
SEE THE NEXT PAGE FOR THE "LOST RECORDS CONTEST" WINNERS!!
I COULD HAVE BEEN SENT TO EL SALVADOR!

WHAT EVER HAPPENED TO DOPIN' DAN'S RECORDS???

DOPIN' DAN
IN
G.I. LOVE
PART I
"THE PICKUP"
©1980 BY TED RICHARDS
HEY DAN. YOU SEEN THIS BOOK YET, "HOW TO PICK UP GIRLS"?
HA, NAW. BUT IT SURE HAS A HOAKY SOUNDIN' TITLE —
BUTTS
THAT WAS MY FIRST REACTION TOO! BUT IT WORKS! I GOT THREE DATES TH' NEXT TWO NIGHTS!
HEY, NOW DON'T BE GREEDY! HOW ABOUT GIVIN' ME ONE!?
HA! NO WAY! NOT AFTER TH' DRY SPELL I JUST WENT THROUGH! HERE. READ TH' BOOK! IT REALLY WORKS!
O.K. I GOT NOTHIN' BETTER TO DO EXCEPT CLIMB TH' WALLS AROUND HERE ON FRIDAY NIGHT!
HOW TO PICK UP GIRLS
JUST A FEW HOURS LATER!
"— REMEMBER: BE PROUD OF WHO YOU ARE. YOU HAVE NOTHING TO LOSE! YOU CAN ONLY WIN! COMPLETE AND TOTAL CONFIDENCE IS THE SECRET BEHIND APPLYING ALL THE SCIENTIFICALLY PROVEN TECHNIQUES WE HAVE REVEALED THUS FAR — NOW GO GET 'EM TIGER!!"
IF OL' "STINKY" CAN SCORE THREE, I'M GOOD FOR A HUNDRED!
THE BOOK THAT WILL CHANGE YOUR WHOLE DAMN LIFE!
HMM... I FORGOT ABOUT TH' STACKED DECK HERE IN FATALBURG!
WHOOPS! NO NEGATIVE THOUGHTS ALLOWED! THINK POSITIVE! THESE SUCKERS DON'T KNOW WHAT I KNOW!
ACTION
Pink Pussy Cat

"SURVEY THE SCENE. PICK OUT THE GIRL YOU'RE THE MOST ATTRACTED TO. YOU DESERVE THE BEST, SO YOU START WITH THE BEST! NOW, POSITION YOURSELF SO SHE CAN CHECK YOU OUT. DON'T LOOK AT HER! DON'T DO ANYTHING WEIRD OR FOOLISH — JUST BE YOURSELF!"
3
2
THERE! SHE'S TH' ONE! I'M IN LOVE!!
1
"NOW BE ON THE ALERT FOR AN OPPORTUNITY TO CLOSE THE DISTANCE WHILE HER INTEREST LEVEL REMAINS HIGH."
SHE SMOKES! SHE'LL NEED A MATCH!
QUICK! I'LL USE THE "STRIKING A MATCH WITH ONE HAND" TRICK!!
HI! NEED A LIGHT?
SURE...
FLITCH
YEOH! YIPE!!
OH NO! QUICK! PUT YOUR HAND IN MY DRINK!
HEE.. UH.. SORRY. CHEAP MATCHES THESE DAYS... UH.. CAN I BUY YOU ANOTHER DRINK? IT'S TH' LEAST I CAN DO...
SURE, BUT WHAT'S GOING ON HERE? EVERY GUY IN THIS PLACE IS STRIKING MATCHES WITH ONE HAND- BUT YOU'RE TH' FIRST TO GET BURNED!
HA HA HA
HA HA
OH... HA HA... IT'S JUST SOME "NEW CRAZE"— BUT THIS IS TH' FIRST TIME I EVER BURNED MYSELF- HA...
-A CASE OF "GUMBO'S LAW: WHEN SOMETHING CAN GO WRONG, IT'LL GO WRONG AT THE WRONG TIME."!
GUMBO'S LAW?! SOUNDS LIKE MY LIFE!!
HEY, C'MON, YOUR LITTLE STUNT WAS TH' FIRST LAFF I'VE HAD IN WEEKS!

PART II "THE SCORE"
"ONCE YOU KNOW A WOMAN WANTS YOU, DON'T HESITATE TO FOLLOW THROUGH ON THE PICK-UP!
HEY C'MON, LET'S BLOW THIS SCENE!!
RIGHT! THERE'S TOO MANY G.I.'S HERE!
WHAT DO YOU SAY—MY PLACE OR YOURS?
LET'S GO TO YOUR PLACE..
UH..ER..SURE! B-BUT MY CAR'S IN TH' SHOP... AH, WHAT TH' HELL—WE CAN CATCH A BUS -C'MON
O.K., YOU LEAD TH' WAY...
"IT'S A MYTH THAT WOMEN ARE IMPRESSED BY EXOTIC CARS, MONEY AND LUXURIOUS PENTHOUSE APARTMENTS—
FT. FRAGG
—IF A WOMAN WANTS YOU, SHE'LL GO WITH WHAT YOU GOT, SO MAKE THE MOST OF IT!"
C'MON, WE GET OUT HERE!!

THE BARRACKS! COME ON! THIS JOKE'S GONE TOO FAR!
NO! YOU DON'T UNDERSTAND!
KILLER 'B' CO
502
SEE. I GOT A KEY TO THE SUPPLY ROOM! IT'S MY OWN SECRET LITTLE PLACE! IT'S GOT MATTRESSES AND EVERYTHING!
NO. NO. STOP!
LOOK. YOU'RE REALLY SWEET, BUT I-I REALLY CAN'T GO THROUGH WITH THIS... I-I'M GETTING SCARED OUT HERE...
O.K., O.K.! I GET TH' DRIFT. LOOK, I'LL CALL A CAB AND PAY FOR IT!
"NEVER GIVE UP! WOMEN CAN BE FICKLE CREATURES AND EVEN THE BEST PICK-UP ARTIST WILL FAIL TO NET A SCORE! SO COVER ALL BASES AND GIVE HER YOUR PHONE NUMBER- IF SHE WANTS YOU, SHE'LL CALL YOU!!
TH' CAB'S HERE..UH. THANKS AN' SO LONG..
IF YOU WANNA CALL ME, I'M AT TH' 82D AIRBORNE DIV, 502 BTL GP, RAD RANG ICPT, CO'D', RA 246-74-9901, CQ, ROSTER 56- PHONE 62-51-OP-9...
YOU'RE RIGHT STINKY. THIS "HOW TO PICK-UP GIRLS" BOOK REALLY WORKS- NOW ALL I NEED IS A MILLION DOLLARS AND A DISCHARGE AND I'M IN BUSINESS!!
HEY, THAT'S EASY!
JUST READ THIS BOOK "HOW TO GET RICH AND FAMOUS DURING THE COMING APOCOLYPSE!"